Graffiti Narratives

Graffiti Narratives

Poems 'n' Stories

Mike Jenkins

Planet

First published in Wales in 1994 by Planet

PO Box 44
Aberystwyth
Dyfed
Cymru/Wales

ISBN 0 9505188 1 6

Designed by Glyn Rees

Printed by Gwasg Gomer, Llandysul, Dyfed

Contents

Acknowledgements: *Planet; Y Faner Goch; Radical Wales; The New Welsh Review; Songs; Fortnight; The Valleys Poet; Black Har-* vest (ed. John Evans); *The Urgency of Identity* (ed. David Lloyd); *The Independent; Forward Poetry Anthology '93; WTBF!;* Red Poets Society; *Poetry Wales;* BBC Radio Wales. "Gurnos Boy" was published in an earlier version in *A Dissident Voice* (Seren).

Author's note: The section titles to "Graffiti Narratives" come from sets of graffiti on either side of a railway bridge in Merthyr Tudful. The background and characters are entirely fictional.

I'd like to thank the Arts Council of Wales for a 3-month bursary which enabled me to write a number of these poems and stories.

Published with the financial support of the Arts Council of Wales.

mong the Debris

Ee were a brill teacher, ee were.
Ewsed t' tell us stories
of is time in the navy.
Playin cards underwater
is leg trapped in a giant clam.

But every so often
ee'd go mental, throw a wobbly,
grabbin ower desks an chairs
as we woz scribblin appily
an fling em flyin
is eyes explodin like gas,
is screams pick-axin
into ower yer-drums,
ower mouths woz gulpin,
we wuz so stunned!

An arfta, ee always passed
a bagfull o' sorries round,
tellin us ow ee still
could yer that sound:
a slow, unnatural thunder
of movin ground an ow
ee wuz searchin fer them lost children,
buryin is ands in slurry
till ee found us, sittin
among the debris.

mouthy

Sborin, sir!
We're always doin racism.
It's that or death, sir.
Yew're morbid, yew are,
or gotta thing about the blacks.

But sir mun! Carn we do summin intrestin
like Aids or watch a video o' *Neighbours*?
Mrs Williams Media upstairs ave got em.

Oh no! Not another poem!
They're always crap, rubbish
not enough action, don' rhyme.

Yer, sir, this one's got language in it!
It's all about sex!
Yew're bloody kinky yew are!
I'm gettin my Mam up yer.

Sir! We aven done work frages,
on'y chopsin in groups.
We ewsed t' do real English
when we woz younger,
exercises an fillin in gaps.

Sir mun! Don' keep askin me
wha we should do,
yew're the bloody teacher!

The

The las pit in Wales,
las dolphin in-a sea.
Slike a volcano
top of a diamond mine,
I jus fail t' see
wha's be'ind theyr bullshitocracy.
Will some whizz-kid arrive
in is capital plane
an save us all from pain?
Are they puttin-a boot in
t' the goolies of-a working-class,
kickin-a once rebels up the arse?
Coz there's ardly any fight left:
we're staggerin down 'n alley
lookin f' coins in-a dark
an the ground's all manky
with-a spew of industry
slippin us, limbs wheelin.
The las pit in Wales,
las red kite in-a country.
Slike a fault-line runnin
right through ower omes:
this int no vandalism
it's an act of atrocity.

Las · pit

Murderer

Ee didn bother no-one.
Woz quiet as a muzzled alsatian.

In school the teachers
give im jip
coz ee never answered
no questions.
Sat there like a snake
tryin t' blend
inta the background.

The kids couldn leave im be,
called im "Poofter!"
an wound im up
like a clockwork toy.

"Yew're soft as shit!" they'd say,
but once when ee got bigger
I seen im clock a teacher
oo said there wuz more life in beans.
Ee never said nothin agen.

At ome ee spent is time
doin up ol cars.
Treated em as if ee wuz courtin.
The tool ee'd andle
woz a spanner not is ol boy!

When I yeard ee'd stabbed er
I woz amazed.
Ee'd kept it inside
all em years.

4

She wouldn leave im ave it, see.
Ee ardly knew er.
Washed the blood off is ands
at work, like ee'd take off
oil an stuff with swarfega.

graf

"UP TO £50,000 GO FISH!"

With a paintbrush fist
I wuz no bullshit artist,
anglin off-a bridge
thinkin o' them cars
I'd catch the days arfta:
missin all-a trains
tippin my brain
over-a parapet.
Ow I'd take theyr eyes
an jerk em upward:
boy with a broken rod,
boy with an ol man
oo drove like mad.

Found a ledge o' rock
found a rush o' river
found some shady trees
but the road come arfta me,
ewge pillars like is legs
an up in-a clouds
I could yer em engines
an a fog o' fumes risin.
But the water woz pewer
so's I could ardly remember
the town an trolleys
an rat-bite rumour.

I ad t' go further
where there wuz no signs t' follow
up-a Taf Fechan's small gorges

NARRATIVES

where on'y the swallows
could balance above-a water,
oldin my rod alone
untin fer a place never seen
no wheel, searchin f' summin rare.

Come to an openin
come to grassy flat banks
river broader 'n' shallower
the light wuz skinny-dippin.
Seen a couple there
er legs wide as a grin,
is back bare an gleamin
like a fish's side,
I seen theyr kid
wanderin an paddlin
as 'ey rocked in rhythm
t' the liquidy sun:
ee coulda bin drowned
fer all they cared.
I wanted t' ook im away
an tell im ee wuz me.

Then, jus when-a ouses
emerged over-a skyline
an the path resembled tarmac,
I seen this log stretched
like a crocodile from bank t' bank.
'Cross like a circus act
these kids 'n' dogs wuz temptin,
teasin theyr feet an laughter
become all colours in a bridge
I couldn leap on, but I knew
this woz the one, a dragonfly
still livin I ewsed f' bait,

an oak rod, reed line,
ever'thin ad t' be right.

It wern so easy
coaxin it away,
seemed t' belong there
arched with theyr joy.
An then I finally caught it,
coulda sworn I seen
the indigo an scarlet
bleed down, makin em silent.

I run like a nutter with it
jarred like frogspawn done in school,
never minded no traffic
pavements didn bring me down.
This woman she grabs me
(pissed outa er skull)
"Le's ave a look, sonny?
Wha yew got there then?"
I swung er away, thinkin o' mam
an ow she couldn say nothin
to im, ow maybe them colours
coulda brung back er speech.

Took it to-a fishmongers
jus t' get it weighed
"Aye, there's a rainbow, son,
but wha appened to-a trout?"
Took it to-a laboratrees
t' see if it wuz rare
an they tried t' slice it open
but the colours all went dirty.
Took it to-a surgree
t' try an get it ealed

but the doctor says, "You're crazy!"
when I tol im it wuz truth revealed.

Took it to-a cemetree
placed it by er stone,
waited fer er voice t' free
watched the evenin sun
bring them colours back agen,
yeard er voice whisperin t' me
"One day they'll be payin
50,000 pound f' fish, my lovely
an wha yew got there
int worth nothin ardly:
cept it's risen me up
an give me summin.
Now take it back
t' where it do belong."

Arfta, it swum straight inta
the air by-a river,
I'm shewer I yeard dogs 'n' kids
in the echo o' green an silver:
it formed a bridge once agen
though I could never walk over,
so's I went with darkness, my on'y friend,
t' make ower headlines,
t' make em wheel-fiends wonder:
my dead mam's words prophesyin,
takin minds away from destinations
makin em troubled fer explanations.

2

"STRIP HAIR, I, JUNK ROT PLACEBO"

Wrote it with a knife
dipped in black paint,
the blood o' myself
coz I'm darkness see.
Not the blade meant fer im,
but the one I nicked
from-a ospital where
they'd cooped me up.

Never slept without a touch
ard an sharp under my pillow
arfta ee ad me tha time:
stabbed is flabby flesh
once in a dream,
feathers panickin upwards.

It woz my air done it see.
Soon as it grew
ee come fer me
like some dog on eat.
An she jus screwed up er face
screamin quiet, "Don' yew ever
say nothin t' nobody!"
She never even cwtched me.

Oo woz there cept my friends
an needles could take me
where nothin could urt?

I wan im t' see

ev'ry time ee's passin,
t' know I'm lost an found,
an experiment failed an succeeded.

I cun 'member takin is razor
an cuttin em off, one by one,
them small airs o' growin,
leavin em round-a ouse
fer er ysterical vacuum mouth
"Yew should be locked up!
I swear yewr on-a drugs!
I'll put yew in-a Omes!"

But she never done nothin,
scared I'd grass on im
an ee kept is ands off
knowin I'd run im through
like a soldier's bayonet
I seen once on-a telly.

Went up-a Funny Farm instead
arfta potchin up school
(kicked out f' writin on walls).
A scheme it woz, an I loved
all em mingin sheds,
pigs 'n' cows 'n' chickens all
with names I give.
Got so close to em
I become a veggie:
my mam jus slagged me off
callin me a moany cow,
I says "Cows 're lush! Thanks a lot!"
She says "Yew cheeky get!"

One day I wuz so pissed off
with thinkin bout all em ens
endin up in supermarket freezers,
I let em free... they took persuadin,
I ends up cluckin at-a manager
an it were nex stop ospital,
all trussed up an plucked
an oo's this mad bird?

It wuz cold turkey there!
Ever bin starved f' days?
Well, tha were me without a fix:
they fed me some substitute shit
but my blood craved arfta it,
my ead wuz a cage o' noises
all clamourin t' get out.

Till I met this boy, see.
Tol me ee wuz in voluntree,
arst me why I ad patches
in my air, I says
"It's all weeds an no edges,
I pulled up some, but plenty remains.
They're givin me poison!"
Is eyes flicked on, ee understood
like no shrinkin doctor could.

"Take these," ee says, "stuff called placebo.
But don' let them nurses know."
An ee takes out these pills
looked jus like Smarties.
"These 're rainbow's eggs, see?"
"Yew... yew mus be loopey!"
"Well, wha *yew* doin yer?"

They tasted sweet 'n' chocolatey
so's I thought it were a lie:
then I tugged at my air
an it come out in bunches,
threw its strangle-cords away.
"Now I wan summin from yew."
I'd 've give it im then 'n' there
on a ospital bed with-a nurses watchin
but ee says, "I need darkness.
I'm gunna tell-a world... well, anyone
oo stares up an notices."
"I'll go darkness. I cun ang
upside down. We'll go together,
I got my own plans."

I tatooed it in stone
fer my ol man's skin
an I scratched it long,
the las strands fell like feathers.
Ee eld me tight, I trusted im
"Tomorrow," ee says, "we'll go up-a river."

I'm tellin yew they're off theyr trolleys!
A whool famlee o' nutters!

I seen em through a gap
in ower Vesuvian blinds
with all theyr comin's an goin's:
I'd rather them Rastafarasians
smokin... what-yew-call... grass 'n' leaves.

They play in the street
with all the kids (cept owers, o' course):
I think they're mentally efficient.
Course, I never let em ave theyr ball back,
just t' teach em a lesson.

They d' play piano loud ev'ry evenin
as ower baby's goin off, what timin.
They sing in Welsh an all:
I'm shewer they belong
to them Sons of Glenfiddich.

Why carn they ave a satellite saucer
like everyone else? There's effin 'n' blindin,
it's all in my diary, written down.
An even theyr anky-panky sounds
like a cage o' monkeys.

We're Merthyr born 'n' bred.
They come from bloody Aberdare!
They don' pay theyr poll tax
an let off fireworks in the New Year.

I'm tellin yew, we're goin off ower trolleys
now theyr eldest's learnin violin.
We ave t' turn up ower telly...
an t' think, we woz once a musical nation.

ONCE A MUSICAL NAT

Ol Orse Features

We wuz up-a Morlais
nickin golf-balls
when I seen it:
red elicopter buzzin
like a dirty great big insect.

"Mus be the Queen!"
I says jokin,
then we seen er
ol orse-features.

She wuz goin abseilin
off the arches,
wish I'd ad
a bow 'n' arrow
I'd 've bin Robin Ood
an sent er flyin.

I on'y think
they should try fer jobs
like the rest of us:
they never paid no poll tax
an ave more olidays
than satellites on ower estate.

We gobbed at er from-a castle,
done V-signs
then legged it rapid,
id in bushes f' cover
with ower small white grenades.

Gurnos Boy

I come from-a ewgest 'state in town,
second ewgest maze in Ewrop, they say,
coz planners potched it up, the clowns:
I'd give em a proper lampin
on'y they've all gone away.

Life gets so bloody borin
I'd sooner read-a graffiti
than stay in-a house snorin:
latest is MAGIC MUSH, writin like spaghetti
thrown over walls, adverts f' sin.

Ower streets wuz named arfta trees
t' make em sound natural, innit?
But yew mostly ave Nature b'yer
when yew tread in-a shit,
or see dogs umpin in threes!

At-a school on top o' the ill
where I ewsed t' bunk if I ad-a chance,
we wore uniform fit fer a funeral,
the on'y way yew could advance
wuz if yew give em no jip, wern a rebel.

The state o' ower ome is beyond:
we got ot an cold runnin water
down-a walls an windows an a pond
in-a livin-room, which we oughta
convert into a tidy sauna.

This place is gettin famous f' murderers,
we produce em like Oovers washin-machines.
If this Government push me much further

I'll afta cut them posh people clean
in theyr big ouses with burglar larms.

Carn wait f' Monday t' come round:
Giro cheque droppin like a gulp o' beer
an lastin just as long. The sound
o' money like-a rain tampin down
arfta drought on ower cracked reservoirs.

SNOOKER BAR

We want NO WOMEN YER!
Even if they it the balls
with theyr size 40's
an chalk theyr cues
with lips like rubber dinghies.

Le's keep em on-a calendar
over by the bar.
Le's turn em over
on-a juke box
as we down a few pints.

I don' care if she is a champion.
I don' care if she've ad
twenty breaks of 110.
I don' care if she is a female urricane.

Women do gossip like starlins.
The noise o' theyr voices
crows cross ower yer-drums.
They d' start trouble,
turn mild men inta fightin cockerels.

Besides, there's-a bard language...
the pin-ups on-a walls
they might take ception to...
the question of-a bogs.

No, I int scared o' bein beaten!
But wouldn 'ey ruin my concentration
as I'm takin a shot, while-a other boys
try t' snooker em back inta the kitchen?

ᐱ LOST ON ◇ME

Tips ud bin dozed away
practically overnight, even-a road
didn seem t' know which way
it wuz goin.
The moon struck me
coz them ills wern there
no more an-a gypos
ad cleared off from notches
between em, bits o' clinker
shone like-a stars.

What ud seemed so certain green
wuz now grey-black-brown
like-a ashes o' mornin.
Them streaks o' red
woz-a blood of iron
they'd swab up soon.

An-a village ad bin opened up:
the two ol coal-line bridges
tumbled an rubbled, so's-a lights
looked like sky comin down
to-a Valley bottom.

Gullies fer-a new road
ad bin scooped out t' north 'n' south
an my westerin, sweatin toil
up-a steep ill wuz alted:
one way sea, the other Beacons.

It were on'y when I seen
a-terraces trackin my direction
an them "For Sale" signs like steps

GROUND

I trod on... it were on'y-a pub's
arfta ours shady curtains
an-a posh ouses with livin-rooms
fer cars stuck on, at got
the teeth o' my keys chatterin.

Ol Shakey

(For KS3 and all who sink in her!)

Ol Shakey does my ead in!
Why didn ee write tidy?

I mean, sall about bloody fairies.
They do belong on a Christmas tree.

Tha Puck... oo's ee or is it she?
A misprint or wha?

An as fer Oberon,
I reckon ee's arfta Bottom!

Ernia? She'd give yew one.
Titania? Didn she ave a toy boy?

See, I never knew it wuz all about
bonkin till ee tol us.

Mind, I'd rather-a English version
in them Brodies notes.

Ol Shakey musta bin on-a magies!
Love potion? More like Ecstasy.

"Kinky sex with an ass-head man
in a wood outside Athens."

When I wrote tha in-a exam
I got absolutely nothin.

The whool of Oovers
with a vacuum ahead of em
facin the sack
coz no-one's buyin.

Merthyr Vale's not even rubble
not even a museum,
they've cleared up the past
t' try an stop us seein.

Coz they're greenin it over
shiftin the slag
changin the land:
they carn bring it back.

Thorns is a cracked bulb
angin on the ill,
not a shade fer decoration
all the lines still.

The brick factree's deserted
cept fer stacks o' bricks,
igh-rise flats they are
f' mulgies of insects.

An they're greenin it over
talkin numbers don' make no sense,
plantin every word
but there's always a fence.

Greenin it over

They sent im ome, Dai Oxo,
with is close-crop barber's chop,
claimin ee wuz a bard example.

Ee ardly done nothin wrong
with is innocent grin
an pick 'n' shovel sayin's.

Ee never jumped no-one,
ee never called em rotten
with is specs an funny ways, Dai Oxo.

Ee wuz just a skin without-a aggro
years arfta they woz fashionable:
ee didn fit inta theyr "normal".

They promised im a tidy reference
if ee didn go to the press:
suspend im if ee made eadlines.

If ee'd bin a pupil they'd 've put im
in a room till it grew... "But how
can you have a shaved head in this profession?"

They said, in suits and ties, respectably
filin lies an always forgettin
the ones oo'd light up the school.

Dai Oxo

JoyRider

I get such a buzz,
better 'an speed isself, it is,
an money fer-a wheels.
Sometimes we jus burn out
when we think-a cops 're arfta us.

Didn tha politician say
"Get on your bike!"
Well, we done it ower way.
An arf a tennis-ball an screwdriver
is all I need
t' take me anywhere.

Till... would yew believe?
My own gran grassed on me!
Aye, she seen me up-a shops
doin a Fiesta with-a boys.
Got grounded f' months I did.

"Won' ever do it agen!"
Tha's wha I tol-a law.
But there int nothin better
'n racin down-a road
with a car fulla fanny an draw.

Is Innocent.

See this medal, mun?
Got it fer asslin-a Paddies,
searchin-a Micks,
uprootin ouses, dirty tricks.

See these engravin's, my name?
Like a minted coin it is,
ne' mind the Queen.
Wish I could spend it sometimes:
carn do nothin now
with tincan leg, buggerall compensation.

Oled up in a bogs we woz,
lovely barb-wire fencin
an women galore... on walls:
plenty o' one and dancin.

I musta bin darft or summin:
in cadets they tol us
the IRA wired up babies.
But I seen a butty
like a butcher's window in seconds.

Got my leg from-a Falklands:
a little souvenir, see?
From shaggin too many penguins!

Naa! The bloody Sir Galahad!
Well, we wuz on'y Taffies.
They shifted ammunition before us:
we wuz left in-a pit of-a ship
with ower sweat goin canaries
an the stink of terror
like shit from-a Phurnie.

Eero? Well, I never seen us win.
Arf-dead in ospital I woz
an bin tha way since then.

Veteran

NOVELTIES

I'm fed up of-a boredom. Yer I am perched like a pigeon, cept if I'd bin one ee mightn't 've left, coz ee spent all is time up in em lofts. An I wuz is omer, always returnin whatever. She's is tumbler, is bit o' fluff, is fancy woman. Performin all kinds o' tricks t' please im.

I ewsed t' love this view cross-a narrow valley, shakin ands with-a Aberbeeg Road, them neat little lofts b' there like tiny ouses. The bracken curlin in autumn like Nature's perm. Now, I ate it all! It's a bloody armpit an a man's one at that! It reeks o' stale booze, it's a loada tufts between slopes tha ardly let in-a sky. The road's so twisted down towards Cwm, it's like one of em metal puzzles I do put in sometimes. The on'y new thing appenin up yer is roadworks. Look at them trees, so forlorn. I know it's coz of the time o' year, but yew'd think they wuz dead if yew didn know better.

The on'y bits I d' like, is them two crops o' rock. They remind me of ol Westerns, cliffs stickin outa deserts. If I could get away, I'd take them with me! What a darft thought.... "Got anything to declare?"... "Aye, two dirty great big lumps o' rock."

Oh well, back t' bloody work. Snap, twist, lick. Drivin me crackers! Jus the sort o' joke.... Tha's me, bit o' silvery paper. I still got it, but oo wants a woman o' thirty-odd with a couple o' kids? Might as well be a prisoner. I 'member seein tha jail in Swonzee, thinkin o' prisoners lookin out t' sea with ev'ry wave repeatin "Free, free". A lot of cack on-a beach there they say. Mind, I'd still like t' live overlookin-a Bay, with tidy shops nearby. All we got round yer is-a Spar.

A joke, a ring. I don' wear it no more. Not tha ee'd notice if ee wuz still yer. "What d' yew call a man oo fancies pigeons?...." "A pervert!" With this ring, I thee name. Ne mind, tonight's the night!... Trish... she's orright an er usband's great. I even seen im doin-a ironin! Now Chris woulda called im a "bender", but ee's almost tha New Page man. Course, ee d' get jealous, mind, an Trish as t' be in when ee says. But at least she gets out now an agen.

Put on yer paper at, we're goin t' ave a party! I'm gunna look real sexy... tight skirt an silky white blouse. Do my face up tidy. Six lagers an I'll be flyin igh. Won' feel like comin home at all. A big man from somewhere foreign. Jamaica or summin... passin through with is reggae band. Or Cardiff even... "Why don't you come for a drive in my car, young woo-man?"... The way ee'd say it, real slow, enough t' make yewr juices flow... "I know jus the spot. Beyond Trefil... there's a disewsed quarry... I ewsed t' do my courtin...."

My ands achin like I've got arthritis orready. Bent over this table. I'm sick of it! It's time I got-a kids.... "Mam! Mam! Cun we pull one?"

Tha's one thing I'm not goin t' buy this Christmas. We'll make ower own. It's easy kids. On'y we'll do it tidy, not like these yer rip-off things. We'll ave real magic fish inside tha glow an go all colours accordin t' wha yewr future's goin t' be. My fish 'll go green. What'll tha mean? Sickness or a change o' scene?

"Leave them bloody crackers alone, will yew? I tol yew before! Bloody ell they get ev'rywhere!... If I lose them, I lose money an bloody Santa don' come coz I gotta pay fer im same as evry'thin."

An Darren looks at me all knowin an says, "As Santa got bailiffs too, Mam?" Der, tha boy's got 'n ead on im fit f' Mastermind! Don' know where ee d' get it from. Not from me. Words never bin my strong point.

Out on-a town, gettin it down. Kids dumped on my mam. Jus fer once, mam love. It's on'y me an Trish. No arm.

"Ow's trade, Deb?"

"Wish I wuz goin t' be pulled like them flamin crackers, Trish!"

"Yew never know yewr luck!"

An we larf. If ower larfs ad wings they'd 've taken us t' Florida. Not tha I wanna go there. Mickey bloody Mouse? Too much like what I do fill em with.

Two young men on-a untin expedition. All glossy sportswear.

"Goin joggin, boys?"

"Either of yew from Jamaica?"

"Yew mus be pissed!"

Bonkin in-a disewsed quarry! Ow romantic! Back seat with furry covers (imitation, o' course!)

"Trish! Le's go up-a club!"

She looks so funny when she's pissed. Er eyes d' pop outa er ead. Er face is like plastocene!

"The club?"

"Yeah!"

"The Comrades?"

"Neow! Habergavenny Glof Club!"

I says, tryin t' talk real posh an gettin all-a words wrong, as usual.

"The on'y time a woman goes into the Comrades Club is t' clean-a bogs out, Trish. Are yew takin the piss?"

"I don' care! We'll show em!"

"Are yew prepared?"

"'Ow d' yew mean? Ave I got a packet o' condoms?"

"Na! I mean ave yew got a machine-gun?"

The long road t' the Comrades. Chippie on-a way. Followed by-a two fitness freaks with-a spare bellies. Maybe I put too much scent on! I trip on-a step outa the chippie an one of em tries t' come to the rescue. Trish throws im a chip.

"Yer! Tha's the on'y bite yew'll ave tonight!"

As we larf agen an walk away they tell us t' "Fuck off, yew slags!" an the Comrades come just in time. They don' follow us in coz they think we're goin t' get ower ol men in there.

Me an Trish like two bloody Martians landin. Ower stockin'ed legs showin up like antennae. Them male ewmans gawpin. The silence before an explosion, an then... nothin nasty, but loads o' comments comin at us from all sides. Even-a barman says, "Wha yew want, love? Or need I ask?"

"Is this really 1991?" Trish says, gettin stroppy, "or ave we gone back a century?"

Oo should appear, comin from-a bogs, zippin up an burpin with all-a manners of a runaway juggernaut, but Chris!

"Bloody ell, Debbie! Wha yew playin at? Yew finally flipped, or wha?"

So I grab-a nearest pint an flung it in is gob!

"Tha's fer ol time's sake!"

We run out, gigglin like mad. Ower noise seems t' spin the

town like one o' them ol-fashioned tops. The pavements wobble to a stop, so we run till we caught up with-a expression on is face. Stunned! It ud bin like I'd undressed im in front of the boys an made is willy shrink t' the size of a peanut.

We run in-a direction of Trish's ome. I'm drinkin the air an it tastes better 'n all them lagers.

Suddenly, Trish catches old o' my arm an pulls me to an abrupt alt.

"Deb! I thought I seen em boys!"

"So? Didn yew fancy em?"

"Don be darft, I'm a married woman!"

"So wha? This is ower fling, init?" An I flap frantic once agen, till I come to a ewge sign. It's brandnew an as the face of a clown on it. It says "This way to 1992."

I think I'm seein things, but Trish reads it out loud. Its arrow points towards a rough track which jus leads t' ol waste-tips. Although er ouse is nearby yer, I notice now tha Trish is shittin erself. She musta really seen them boys an thinks theyr followin us.

"Deb! Le's go up my ouse an ave a couple there, eh?"

I'm beyond though. My ead's still up above, circlin.

"C'mon. Don' be borin! This is the path to the future! Let's go an see what it brings!"

She squeezes my arm so tight it urts bard. She stares so ferocious, I think she's goin t' slam me one.

But I shake myself free an stumble up-a uneven track. All-a time I'm ascendin inta dark, I yer er shoutin while I keep goin up.

Steps be'ind me. Them boys agen! I run inta the night. It pulls me down with its weight. There int no future yer, the ground's broken, the track disappears! I cun yer my eart clear. Fer ev'ry beat there's a step. My ankle gives way, twists, I slide an tear my tights. Oh bugger! I feel-a skin scraped on my leg.

I lie listenin. Nothin cept-a sound o' car engines risin up-a valley-slopes like smoke. Maybe they've gone back, given up chasin. Woz tha sign theyr little trick, theyr joke t' lead us away?

But it int us, it's on'y me. I know ow them trees feel I cun see from my window. Might as well be them: fixed, lonely an waitin. Fer wha? Birdsong?

I'm bloody freezin! Put my ands in my coat-pockets. Oh no! I don' believe it! Two crackers! The kids musta...

Le's ave a celebration, Deb. After all, this is 1992, almost a month before it's yer. What's goin' t' come out? My wages? Now that ud be a real joke!

"Wha d' yew call a cracker-worker oo earns buggerall?"

"Desperate Debbie."

So I take one end in one and an one in-a other an... phut! Like avin it off with Chris! Not with a bang, but a wimp (I read tha once in school, I'm shewer). I wipes my leg with-a at. Where's-a toy? Bet there int one. Typical! Oo made this crap?... Oh aye, it were me!

No, there it is. Wha's tha? I don' member puttin tha in. A tiny Japanese pagoda. Ow useless cun yew get? I bury it in-a coal rubble an fist it down.

Well, le's try the other... Pull... Snap! Tha's a better one. Wha d' yew drink at a party on-a slag-heap?"

"Coca Coal-a!"

An-a toy this time's just as weird. A train on-a bit o' string. I think tha cun join-a pagoda.

I'm knackered. I uddle up an don' care no more. Even Trish left me t' go ome t' er darlin an a cup o' cocoa. I dig my eels inta the loose surface like I'm tryin t' put my roots down. I close my eyes. I'm givin up flyin, coz in the end yew always land somewhere like this. Jus waste on-a waste dump. An I can't grow yer coz there's no soil an anyway, oo'd come t' look at me? The kids ud climb fer a short time, my mam ud water an care... I got this strange sensation o' them two novelties growin even outa this wilderness an then collapsin agen as if they'd never bin there. Next year I'll look this way an they'll be the size o' factrees. But fer all tha, they'll jus be balloons. Burst inta nothin.

My fingers feel fit f' breakin, like rotten twigs. I pick myself up an try t' stagger back. If this is next year, I won' be followin no signs in future. Wha wuz-a clown smilin bout? Sick, I reckon.

Even when I yer Trish's voice callin me from-a distance, it don' make me feel no better. Seems like I bin away frages. I'm torn up an flung away, like them boys ud caught up an abused me. I goes blubberin inta Trish's arms like a baby.

"Deb, love! Wassa matter?"

She pats my back as though she wuz windin me!

"Trish, I jus ad a funny experience with a train an a pagoda!"

32 "Yew mean yew jus ad too much lager!"

We giggle agen like a couple-a ens. Then we walks up er ouse arm in arm an er ol man gives er stick fer gettin back so late. I begin t' wonder if ee int like all-a rest of em.

Finally, I collapse on er sofa with-a las vision o' Chris's face soppin an drippin beer. I smile asleep like I never done before.

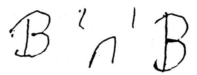

B 'n' B

Ow it ewsed t' be,
Barry Islan an Porthcawl:
ad enough till my dad's redundancy
t' chance a Bingo all.

Them little boxes o' treats,
breakfasts the size o' waves:
the sea ticklin yer feet,
the Shows a dazzlin maze.

A ring I won o' plastic gold,
ring I ewse now f' cans o' beans;
bed I boated, never growin old,
now I see mould in ev'ry dream.

All-a time Deb 'n' Craig shiver
an my body carn warm em,
it's like when I 'member
comin from water, no towel welcomin.

B 'n' B, them letters jus larf at me
ev'ry day from-a angin sign,
like-a landlord's pass at me,
thinks I'll sell im mine.

Deb 'n' Craig screamin, bangin from-a top,
bolt on-a door screw loose,
nobody calls-a cops:
ower radiators run on booze.

Sun on-a steps an pavement
this is ower promenade:
gnawin fingers bout-a rent
on Dogshit Boulevard.

Flasher

Listen t' me gul,
I tell yew ee done it!

They wuz small guls,
didn know nothin.
Ee could've ad
a Jumbo Sausage
down is y-fronts
fer all 'ey cared!

Screwy they d' call im:
no bloody wonder,
ee's a pervie, a nutter,
ee's fuckin angin.

Know wha ee done? Listen, mun!
Pulled out a long cucumber
t' show em an chase em
(most prob coz is plonker
looks like limp onion!).

Know wha I'd ave done?
I'd 've sliced it up
an spread it with salad cream
an ad it fer supper.

Der!... them guls could be put off
sex f' life and never
touch a bit o' salad agen.

Goin Fast

I gorra tell yew, sir mun,
carn keep it in no more:
now I seen er goin fast
like one of 'em pooer Ethiopians.

See I know wha's up with er,
ow she've tried t' tell ev'rybody,
specially yew oo've bin ev'rywhere:
I think she fancies yew secretly.

It's er ol fella, see.
Aye, I know er famlee seem ordinree,
but I don' believe
in them words no more really.

Well... ee've ad er... y' know, sir...
reg'lar like ee wuz fishin,
she feels an ook inside er:
ev'ry pound she loses coz o 'im.

An I ave t' say, coz yew care...
wha cun we do? It's like on-a telly
an she've come outa the screen:
she's killin erself an I on'y stare.

Nex Time

"Nothing to do in Belfast
We got the army on the street..."

(Stiff Little Fingers)

Nothin t' do in this town
less on ower estate:
it's a skip an a tip,
see the cracks down walls
lengthening with ower ate.

We set light to-a cop-shop
ad lovely roast pig.
Nex time we'll ave a larf
as we fire theyr cars:
I'd like t' try canned pork!

Coz they're always
pickin on us,
slaggin us off
when we gang round-a bench
in the evenin bored
an bruisin-a air with frustration.

"Move on! Shift!"
Where to, copper?
The run-down bus-shelter,
the shed of a kiosk,
the subway glue tunnel
with no way back?

One day they're gunna burn
an I'll keep the ashes

t' bury, fer all em times
they took me in
fer all em crimes
I never done
an-a ones 'ey caught me doin.

Singles Night

It's Singles Night at-a local
all-a women burst in like snow
an the baldy specky D.J.
carn wait t' play em real slow.

The las D.J. wuz a dick'ead
with-a tact of a J.C.B.:
playin "Stand By Yewr Man" an "She's Leavin Ome"
with-a demolition subtlety.

The women buzz o' perfume
the men got sideboards from M.F.I.,
even-a walls are sweatin,
everyone's givin the eye.

A piss-artist Social Worker
carn believe wha ee's seein:
all is clients gathered together,
ee ead-butts the telly screen!

"Fuck yew!" she yells, "I wouldn!"
she's coarse as wire wool.
There's more ex's than on-a coupon,
everyone's on-a pull.

It's Singles Night at-a local,
the Social Worker's lost is ands;
couples leave in wrestlin olds,
loners go ome t' finger stands.

CARRYin ON

Ee's the Ead,
she's an istry teacher.
Der! Think they'd know better!

She does erself up
like a pampered poodle:
yew'd need a pneumatic drill
t' get rid of er.

Ee talks with a twang,
ardly Dowlais Top
where ee d' come from.
Follows er round
on a lead o' scent.

I yeard they woz up-a Res
durin the lunch-hour
doin the extra-curricular.

I yeard she spins im round
on is revolvin chair
sayin "This is my duty sir!"

Someone seen em in er room
pinned against a poster of Napoleon,
discussin er promotion.

Is Missis musta scrubbed it out
of is cream shirts f' years:
an lipstick run from the wound
where she'd ad is pecker.

TESCO'S ARDWARE

It were in Tesco's downtown
Sooper Weejee ad im
(they call im tha
coz ee's a Third Dan).
I yeard from is cousin,
so it mus be genuine.

Opkins ad it comin a long time:
ee's a pimp, a dealer in blow
an ee've done more carryin on
than tha Crawshay ever done.

Ee wuz chuckin cans o' corned beef
an soup fer protection.
Some woman rammed em all
with er trolley, I spect
she wanted t' get
to the checkout bardly.

Sliced meat everywhere ee tol me:
Weejee's mob ad machetes, crowbars
an all kinds of ardware.
If they'd jumped im in Texas
they'd 've ad no bother!

Sgettin like ower China
in-a las century:
oo needs them video nasties?
They'll all end up killin one another
an 'en it'll be a case o' Number One
solidest dead man in Merthyr.

THE DAVIES GANG

Wha a larf! Me, live on telly! But I couldn smile even then. Never ave bin able to. Musta bin ammered inta me by the ol man. Wayne coulda done it great, o' course. Yew just ad t' look at im t' crease up in them days at school.

Goin live! I coulda looked straight at em friggin cameras an slagged em all off, them bastards oo laid inta us. My so-called father, oo never give a toss, among em. Why did ee ever ave kids at all, tha's what I'd like t' know?

But I didn. An I didn stammer neither, though my eart wuz beatin like a copper wantin to get in an search a place over. I jus tol em calmly bout me: tha special school in Bridgend where they showed me ow t' old a pen with pride. Prince Charles's scheme. Meetin im an them kids oo woz doin it an all. My stories an poems I wrote fer people on the 'state. Writin fer the baby in the womb, fer my friend's weddin. Whatever... I ad a go at it. My brothers in jail, both of em. Ow I coulda gone the same way on'y...

An tha's all my dad yeard of the whool interview: Chris 'n' Wayne. Chris 'n' Wayne.

Ow could yew? Oo d' yew think yew are? Some kinda fuckin star?

I think ee wuz jealous, y' know. Ee'd like to ave bin there, talkin bout is bloody opera records, is attic full of em.

Bet they ate me now. Most prob they seen it in Portland an in Swonzee.

Look at im, Carl Davies, my bro', mouthin off on-a box like some fuckin politician! Oo do ee think ee is anyway?

An Chris, it coulda bin yew. Yew ram yerself so fulla crap, yew ardly know night from day. An Wayne, yew coulda bin a stand-up comic, no problem. Made Owen Coyne seem like a lump o' lead with is pathetic jokes bout chinkies an spew.

Wha did we do, boys? We worked like a team, a famlee gang. We wuz the Crays up 'n' comin, the 'state's James gang. We slashed tha wanker's tyres coz them teachers wuz always pickin on us. Oh aye! So wha a great act it woz! I wish I'd given that school a bloody chance now. I wuz wild. They couldn tell me nothin an a belt round-a ead on'y made me crazier inside.

I climbed. 'member boys? I scaled em wall-bars like bloody Spiderman an registration woz gymnastics over-a desk. I couldn stand a second my body wern doin summin t' get my juices goin. Even the coppers couldn reach me once. They chased me an I monkeyed up one of them tall lamposts along-a new road.

Come down, Davies! Jump!

They'd 've bin appy t' see me in pieces over-a pavement. The fuckers ad t' starve me down!

Now yer I am on crutches. Pride comes before a slide. Wanted to impress er kid, see? So I says, "Look at me, Jason!" There I goes, arse over tit, the great never-ave-been gymnast breakin my leg on ice. Jason woz really appy. Ee pissed isself an so did Julie, till I never got up. She's pregnant an ad a job liftin me, so's I thought she wuz goin t' ave a miscarriage on-a spot. Lovely place f' one, the ill down t' the Blue Pool an an even better one f' crackin yewr leg in arf. From Prince Charles Award t' Prince Charles ospital! Surprised I didn end up in-a new Maternity Ward!

Wayne! 'member the milk, mun? Tha wuz one of-a best yet. Should've got 'n enterprise award f' that. Spotted a demand, din we, eh? Trailin round them wards with all-a nicked bottles, supplementin theyr diet o' lumpy mash an runny jelly.

Think I'm gunna get pissed. Get tanked up an when I do anythin cun appen!

Anythin did appen!

I collected em round me, don' ask me ow! It wuz like 'ey wuz pushin me on. Great fuckin celebrity... I thought I'd show em!

Pint arfta pint arfta pint. Legless an mindless an ready t' join my two... Glass wern nothin.

"Go on Carl boy! Fer ol time's sake! Put-a boot in!"

An tha bloody plaster which had weighed me down like a ball 'n' chain become the ideal glass-breaker. Usin resources at and, eh Chris? Yew wuz always-a one with-a brains. The things yew could do with-a single screwdriver! Everythin cept openin up yewr own ead. Yew cun do tha with-a needle now, is it?

So I jus put my foot through an they all dived in, vulturin-a shop window. I didn get nothin. I done it f' yew two, see? Couldn stand bein such a mammy's boy!

Mam! I'm sorry! Yewr the on'y one oo gives a damn bout me. I know tha. I'm finished with all tha. I'm on-a right track from now on. They jus disrailed me, them boys. I ad t' bust up all tha telly crap inta shards o' glass.

I know mam, yew never understood. Yew've struggled all yewr life on ands 'n' knees scrubbin-a floors fer-a pittance.

I tol em, the pigs. I stood up igh fer all of us. Leave off my brothers!

"Oh, so yewer the one on telly? Call this goin straight, sonny?"

I spat it all out at em from up on tha table, mam. There wuz no way they were gunna slag off Chris an Wayne. Oo d' yew think yew are, yew fuckin pig bastards!

"Yew'll see them soon enough, Davies boy!"

Mam! I wrote a poem fer-a baby in Julie's womb. I know yew'd like it even if some of-a words ud sound strange. I'll write stories fer the baby an Jason when theyr older. They'll be presents like no others. Julie's lovely, mam, but she'll never ave me. She don' trust no-one. She've been beat up bardly by er ex, see. Oo cun blame er?

I know yew care, but yew never bothered neither. I coulda killed some copper an all's yew'd 've said woz "Tha's orright, son!" If yew'd cared enough, yew'd 've come t' court with me. Ee's the other extreme, in ee, the ol man! Is idea of-a tellin off is a quick kick in-a groin!

"Craig, yew silly fucker! Fancy lettin em catch yew! An yew didn even nick sod all, yew dull twat!"

Boys! Lookin back, we wuz a legend! But like all legends the endin's are tragic. Chris full of oles, like Bonnie an Clyde. Wayne tryin t' cut yerself up... oo wuz tha comic?... oh aye, Tony Ancock.

Nobody'll write bout us though. Nobody'll make films. An it won' be me, coz I wanna get away from it, see? Like-a distance between a boggin estate with its packs o' mangy strays an-a streams an trees of-a Beacons. I wanna catch autumn leaves fallin an write down theyr colours so's they don' blow away.

If I sound like a fuckin poofter, well too bard I say. Coz where's it all got us, eh? All-a friggin eadlines? We never done nothin worth a penny!

Me an Wayne nickin tha JCB an eadin fer Swonzee, when Chris wuz in there fer-a first time. The on'y criminals t' try an break inta a prison! An gettin inta Social Services t' find out what ower files said. When they tried t' take Chris away inta Care on is own, we sat on-a road in front o' tha car, din we?

When I think back on them things now, I think, Wayne, those 're yewr stories. What yew coulda done with them, standin in front of-a microphone don' bear imaginin! Mine 're all bout animals an rainbow bridges an tunnels inta the mountain with magic creatures at the end. Sounds like I'm trippin, but I'm not on-a magies.

I'd break my arm an all, t' get a larf out-a Jason. I'd write bout love in my own blood f' Julie. I'd do a lullaby yew'd call soppy t' welcome er ome with er little one.

But I'm not goin down. I'm not grabbin old of wha int mine no more. Coz even if it's-a on'y way out of-a grime, I'd sooner ewse my pen an-a rickety ol typewriter I picked up at-a local Jumble.

Boys! I'm not puttin yew down. Yew should take back what yewr deservin an I don' mean wha yew'd call ower share, coz tha's all in-a posh ouses by-a river. I mean-a wasted years, before yewr brain-cells 're turned inta mulch like piled leaves, Chris, an before there's no joke worth tellin when yew've strangled yerself, Wayne.

Hey, c'mon! The Davies Brothers! We could do it all different! Do it agen!

The fence

They're buildin a fence surroundin it,
they've flogged off-a rugby pitch:
there'll be no way up the Ooch
on my mountain bike an my dog
'll afta ewse-a multi-gym!

Tha fence is all green at-a front
t' match the facsia boards, the back's
grey as pavin-stones. It as
snake-tongues made o' steel.

The las one went in months,
chicken-wire torn off like paper
woz ewsed in ev'ry garden.

I'll find a way t' bunk.
I seen tha film "The Great Escape".
I'll leap from-a caretaker's roof.
I'll pole-vault ev'ry Games.

No watchtower eads
or machine-gun mouths
'll stop me doin a runner.

I don' give a fuck
if I'm spiked t' death,
I ate being screwed down
by all em words an numbers.

Yew gotta run round
like-a ighlights on telly,
give it a welly
arf way t' Penarth.

Don' matter ow skillful yew are,
yew gotta get stuck in
fall over when tacklin,
cover yewr shorts in muck.

I don' care if ee ave got style,
don' care if ee do beat
four of em regular, cun it it ard
an pass more 'an four yards.

Ee should earn is weight in sweat,
mark every blade o' grass,
do slide tackles on is arse,
ne' mind them fancy flicks.

I don' care if ee can accelerate.
Oo do ee think ee is
a bloody Ferrari anyway?
Arfter all, my money's is pay.

welly

a

it

give

Skin

There int no cage yew cud put me in
an keep me locked up
with a label stuck on
sayin "Freakshow Fascist Skin".

I know I'm right yew're wrong,
I care more bout animals tested on
than them Pakis with theyr shops
'n' stalls rippin us off an mingin.

All em Paki doctors down Prince Charles
oo live in posh ouses up Brecon,
oo talk to us like they woz grand
in words yew carn ardly understand.

I don think-a blacks cause much prob
(at least they got blow 'n' Marley),
it's them fuckin Pakis with theyr dog curry
oo're stealin all-a white Welsh jobs.

An-a Reds oo like the IRA,
I'd blow em all t' bits!
Ang murderers an child molesters I say
an greasy Mandela T-shirt gits!

Now I'm Sixteen

Well, I come in late
coz I wuz up-a Park
watchin the fight an coppers come
an I lost my watch runnin

an now I'm grounded

my Mam seen me smokin
by-a shops an I tol er
she smokes anyway
the silly ol cow

and now I'm grounded

we nicked a pram
an pushed it down-a sliproad
jus missed a Juggernaut
give my pissed brother a lift ome

an now I'm grounded

my Dad caught me snoggin
by-a bus-stop with this lush boy
oo woz over-age, ee says
yew'll get Aids, yew slag!

an now I'm grounded

me an 'is boy Darren
(they do call im Dazzy)
went to a party
an smoked wacky-backy

an now I'm grounded

I run away to stay
with my best friend Debbie,
but my parents came an grabbed me
sayin they'd kick me out ncx birthday

an now I'm grounded

I swallowed forty magies
ad my guts pumped dry,
woke up in Prince Charles
to a diet o' runny jelly

an now I'm grounded

I smashed a bottle on theyr borin telly
an yelled if 'ey grounded me agen
I'd turn into a friggin Jumbo Jet!
an they called me rotten

an now I'm sixteen.

Nex Door

Nex door? I reckon they'r vampires!
They d' keep theyr blinds drawn
all of-a day an night-time:
I'm takin no chances,
I'm eating plenty o' garlic bread.

My mam says they got pasty faces,
but t' me they'r more like pickled onions.
The on'y time I seen theyr son
ee's oldin a plastic gun:
tormentin is white rabbit
till it done a runner.

Tha bloke nearly run me over:
ee's got a face like Frankenstein's monster,
on'y not so nice like.
My dad says ee's a psycho
an if looks ud kill
ee'd be a mass murderer.

Nex door? They smuggle theyr kids
in an out when it's dark,
they'r so quiet it's creepy.
I s'pose tha's wha it's like
t' be the livin dead.

Ooligans

See, Dad, I never knew they wuz there
them blue ooligans,
coz we wuz swear-singin,
messin round an larfin.

They ad crept up
in a pincer movement,
a bloody planned campaign
with big boots fer kickin.

Na! We didn start nothin!
It woz all sudden as snipers,
my butty took an ammerin
off-a theyr flat-cap leader.

Ee didn stand a chance
coz all-a others laid in:
they wuz draggin im an shoutin
"That'll stop your fuckin swearin!"

So I says "Wha's goin on?"
an another, looks like King Kong,
ee fists me in-a plonker
pissin hisself with "You his solicitor?"

Wha wuz-a coppers doin all 'is time?
Are yew trippin, Dad, or wha?
Oo d' yew think wuz em blue ooligans?
Are yew livin in-a Land o' Song?

Sgreat bein a veggie
coz I cun be witty
when people go on about
all-a food 'ey like.

For example "I love fish" 'ey say
an 'en go inta millions o' ways
t' cook em an ev'ry type
from erring t' salmon t' ake.

"So do I!" I twink t' see
all theyr eyes spottin ypocrisy
"specially a-trout jumpin in rivers
an-a silver rockpool slivers."

"An lamb an chicken Sunday dinners."
"Aye, I seen em eatin grass 'n' grain!"
Sgreat bein a veggie:
a full-time sarky pain!

the veggie

Int Au Bard

We int all bard, see.
There's people yer've bin on telly.
There's tidy decent folk
oo ardly swear, especially on Sunday.
There's a Scoutmaster nex door
always looks arfta the boys.

We int all muggers, see.
There's people yer've got burglar larms
jus like Lakeside Gardens,
oo've got walls t' keep theyr kids in.

There's people yer vote Lib. Democrat
an prefer wine, oo int all
on-a dole fiddlin.
Tha Scoutmaster'll do anythin
fer is tabby cat.

We int all carryin on.
I know a couple bin married
20 years, ee's off bowlin
an she've got er gran'children:
when 'ey meet 'ey get on fine.

We int all inta nickin.
There's people round by yer
ave gone completely UPVC!
I know one young man with a PhD:
mind, ee is workin on-a bins.

Titanomaniac

Ee's a Titanomaniac,
ee's off of is ead,
when there's a fire drill
"Abandon ship!" is what ee says.

When we're lost in-a corridors
what all look-a same
ee do parrot off-a figures
o' survivors an-a dead,
as we're arfta room numbers
ee's countin all-a cabins.

I bet is bedroom's a wreck
o' newspaper cuttin's!
I bet is mam's sinkin
with all em voices ee do put on:
sounds like they come
from-a bottom of-a ocean.

When-a teachers give im stick
fer is octopus poison pen,
I think o' the iceberg
ee cun still see a'ead
an ow everyone got skins
what'll easy be broken.

Things

Them small musky nipples
o' the field —
I sucked em all
an-a milk wuz galaxies
when my ead woz rocketin.

Seen things my dreams never touched —
my eyes wuz two moons orbitin,
ponds wuz-a rings o' Saturn,
the gorse bright as unnamed stars.

Seen things I never imagined —
bin so close to-a sun
in ev'ry wild flower,
I sprung like some astronutter,
ardly any air t' keep me down.

But-a nex time at tha place,
though I wanted t' bray away worries
with-a yer-stretchin noise,
my ead woz mulin!

Even my friends faces surrounded,
sticks o' theyr arms
flailin my ide —
I oofed em, legs jerkin.

I'd turned! Never thought I'd get back —
straitjacket of a bridle, see,
all-a time snufflin-a grass
fer what I ewsed t' be.

Macbeth's drive-in

I wuz walkin ome
up by-a Top Ponds
where the sheep woz performin
acrobatics (I'd jus bin
blowin on-a wacky-backy).

These three thorn bushes
with limbs stickin out
like broken guitar-strings,
all of a sudden turned
inta three weird sisters:
Trace, Deb an Shar
wuz gathered round a bucket
o' steamin, noxious potions.
"We know oo yew are!"
screeches Shar with er feedback voice
"yewr Duane Corder, ad a band
called The Glams. Yew'll go far!"
"Ow about now?" cries Deb
showin er idden berries.
"Naa!" yells Trace, "tha's yewr way!"
As she points er fingers
become prickly ends o' branches.

So I followed tha direction
past the Doggy where apparitions
o' drowned puppies rose up
on a stage o' fog, yelpin
at-a spotlight moon.
I come to a vision,
a neon castle with-a big M.
"Macbeth's Drive-In" it says
an at-a entrance I wuz stopped
by a piss 'ead of a security guard,
oo slurs t' me, "I's no good, see.

Carn get my end up no more.
The whoosh 've done fer me.
My ead d' keep knockin
like a bloody ewge amplifier!"

"I wanna job," I says, "I'll do anythin!"
An Mac the manager ee tol me
I'd problee afto, 'is place
wuz full o' sin: they ad
Murder Burgers dribblin with blood
an Double Trouble Boil 'n' Bubble fries
tha resembled ewman fingers
(I wondered where all em parkers got to
oo'd accidentally nodded off).

Anyroad, 'ey give me-a yer-phones,
I woz-a sound man. Mac Duane
they called me coz everyone
wuz Mac Summin up there.
An as-a night went on
strange things begun t' appen:
a woman in a BMW appeared
an one man spewed inta the microphone:
I give im Macduff nuggets
what lived up to theyr name!

This woman — stonkin she woz —
come agen an whispered in my speaker,
"Mac Duane! I heard all about
those three blasted sisters
you met upon the common.
This place could be ours,
I have such plans!"
"Old on! I on'y started workin yer!"

"Are you a shrivelled peanut or a man?"
(sometimes the sound int clear).

So she tol me ow I adto
stick all 'ese pills in-a workers' Cola
an ack Mac t' death
with-a butcher's knife ewsed
t' scare off local vandalisers
an ow we'd ave ower own
"Drive-In Quick Fit Massage Parlour"
of which, o' course, I'd be king.
An I says, "Oh aye, love, but y'know,
it's all bin done before!"

Macbe

Vote fer us!
We give yew muriels
o' workin men
on-a boards o' derelict buildin's.
We give yew bigger, better
burger ouses opposite
the most floral roundabouts
in Mid Glamorgan.
We give yew three lumps
o' dolled up sculpture
nearby OP's factree
fer on'y seventeen thousand pound
an a unique subsidin pool;
fancy swimmin in ol minin galleries?

Vote fer us!
We give yew trees, trees
an more green 'an yew've got
on all-a council ouse plasterin,
an Arts Centre 'at'll look lovely
flattened fer ower road scheme.
We give yew bowls, bowls
an a prize escalator
opened by a Male Voice Choir,
an ne' mind the youngsters
they got plenty o' bus-shelters.

Vote fer us
an we'll give yew
a posh golf-course on-a muck
where-a dry ski-slope ewsed t' be,
so's Japanese businessmen
cun see what fine caddies
ower workforce make,
we'll even ave a motto

"That's our Boro to a tee!"
An 'member it woz us
what give yew tha new logo:
y'know, Martyr Tudful with er permed air
lookin like a fashion model...
an-a red star (but don' ask me
wha tha's doin there).

Plea

Factree

The men put it there
in theyr ard ats.
Branches woz symmetrical
an criss-crossin,
the roots o' wire.

The women work nights
but never turn inta cats,
theyr eyes carn elp closin
as they pick-a fruit,
theyr ands 're cut up
by growths 'at need prunin,
theyr skin turns rough
coz o' scrapin on-a bark.

On-a ground the children
eap up the arvest
an spray it so's it goes
as red as lipstick-shine.
But inside, seeds 're rottin:
yew couldn even count the facts
they're jus splatters o' puke.

Ev'ry so often yew see im landin:
when ee does the women shiver
as if ee woz the north wind.
Ee int no bird, ee's a bein
with legs like scaffoldin
an call of a siren.
Ee'd never live on-a ground,
ee comes from an igh garden
over-a mountains with laid out
picnic flowers an lawn.

Ee flies away above-a arvest,
followin its movement
along the line of a graph.

Trouble with 'is town is
there's too many clicks 'n' clecks,
y'know what I mean?

The clicks 're a uddle
o' committee men (an a few sop women
t' make the tea)
oo're sly as salesmen:
fair t' yewer face
they rip yew off proper be'ind!
Course, theyr kids get picked
fer everythin, it's like-a Masons
or-a ol school tie system
if yew ask me, it don' matter
ow talented yew are:
yew could be Dylan piggin Thomas
but unless yewr ol man's 'n Eadmaster...

An clecks, o' course, is wha's taken
fer facts round by yer.
If someone oo's a mega-mouth
don' like yew, y'might as well
phone-a Samaritans,
coz yew'll be a child-molestin
wife-batterin flasher in seconds.
I'd round up all em cleckerboxes
an whip em on a wheel
down Igh Street... that'd learn em.

Clicks 'n' Clecks

SOME KIND O' BEGINNING

the sound o' voices rises from-a street. More banterin 'an arguin, but it still brings back tha night. There's too many thin's remind me. Ev'ry time I see Dave on telly playin fer-a Jacks. Ev'ry time I go out to a Club (though tha int often nowadays) an there's a barney.

Puttin on my face, layer 'pon layer, I carn elp thinkin ow she must afta dollop it on t' cover over wha I done. An there by my mirror is-a cuttin. People might think I'm sick or summin, but I jus don' wanna forget. It's a warnin: NEVER AGEN!

Wish I wuz goin out with them girls. Theyr jokin pierces-a glass an ruffles-a curtains. A whool gang of em, I bet, like we woz in Merthyr, me, Nadine, Andrea an Jayne (with a "y" don' forget, she'd say). I long fer theyr voices now, goin up an down like-a mountains an valleys. Funny tha, it's flatter down yer an-a way 'ey talk ave not got the same music to it some'ow.

Mascara, face-cream... owever much I put on, I could never be like er. My teeth stick out in funny ways an I got ooded eye-lids like my dad wuz an owl or summin. I light up a fag an burn an ole just above er ead. I 'member wha ee once said, "Martine, I'm sorry t' tell yew, but yewr breath's mingin... Yew should try an give up." But all em months in the Centre I needed em so much. I'll never stop now, not even if I seen im agen.

The thin's the papers said, an mostly true I know. But oo cun understand all 'at goadin? All 'at gangin up an pickin on me er friends done? It wuz like Cardiff 'gainst-a Jacks, we all knew it wuz gunna go off sometime, but no-one spected I would make it appen.

I blow smoke at er picture. The eadlines blur. I yer my flat-mate Chrissie come in from work: tidy job in-a Travel Agents, all dolled up. She's like me, tryin t' make a new life. She've ad 'n ard time, brought up in-a Omes. Carn understand ow she's so straight-lined though. TV on, cuppa tea next...

"Hey, Martine! D' you want a cuppa?"

"No ta, Chrissie! I'm off soon!"

She knows all 'bout me, but it don' bother er. She reckons er dad done worse thin's than tha to er an er mam.

Tha bloody burn above er hair looks like a friggin alo! I feel like ashin tha photo once an fer all, but instead I stub-a fag out on-a mirror, right where my teeth jut out comical.

Chrissie looks so relaxed in-a sittin room when I enter, feet up an sippin away. As she turns er head fer a moment she reminds me of er, tha beaky nose an pointy chin, but...

"Martine, you look great!" she says, an I do feel ready t' face the world, even though I want more.

"Aye, but oo cares in tha poncy otel?"

"Well, maybe you'll meet someone tonight. Some millionaire soccer star'll be passing through and propose to you over his lasagne!"

"Soccer star?"

"Oh... sorry Martine!"

I larf an she wriggles in er chair an echoes me. Soon it's "S'long!" and "Bye". Me wonderin ow she cun talk so posh with er background an ave survived.

The streets o' Abernedd turnin inta Merthyr by the second. Cack-jumpin an spottin where yesterday's shops ewsed t' be. See-through windows replaced by-a environmentally-friendly sort, perfect fer graffiti an posterin. Local bands like Panic Stations an The Pocket Billiards advertisin gigs. I woz inta football when my friends listened t' the Merthyr equivalents o' them. I woz turned on when Merthyr played the Jacks (Dave wern with em 'en) an stood with Dazzy an the boys chantin an loathin to a pitch where I lost myself.

Wassa time? Shit! Four minutes late an moany ol cow Thorpe'll be bound t' dock me.

Car beeps me. Two boys in overalls, all over painty. Give em a V and see em mouthin off at me.

There it is at bloody last, The Dog and Duck, Abernedd's finest, 3 star, AA. Looks real tidy from-a front an all, but I could blow it open, wha with ol Thorpey an is stingy ways... scrapin-a mould off of fruit an tha ol can-opener sheddin rust!

"Yer! Wha's this in my peas, waitress?"

"Oh, I believe it's some sort o' garnish, sir."

When in doubt, call it garnish, tha's wha ee tol us t' say.

Just as I'm gaspin fer a fag an fumblin in my pockets, Thorpey
ops through-a door t' greet me.

"Martine, you're five minutes late again. It'll have to stop, Marteen!"

Sayin my name like I woz 'n alien. Feel sorry fer is missis, I do. Imagine im on top on the job... "You've had your ten seconds heavy-petting, dear. Now we'd better hurry up and start breathing faster!"

"Marteen! Stop grinning and get ready, will you!"

Soon I'm all frilled up an layin-a tables, all-a time chattin t' Michelle oo on'y jus started las week an oo keeps cockin ev'rythin up. She's so nervous an tryin t' please, but Thorpey give er so much jip when she wrote-a orders down wrong, she nearly give up on er first day. An the bloke what ad steak 'n' kidney pie 'stead o' steak! I thought ee wuz gonna crack er one on-a spot!

Lee, the main chef, ee takes-a piss outa Mich no end. Ee tried it with me when I begun, so I tol Mich t' take no notice. But she don' know when ee's bullin or not. Ee tol er the correct way t' serve chips wuz with a fork an she believed im. By-a time she'd got em on-a plate, they'd frozen agen!

Friday evenin, but it's real quiet. I serve a family with a stroppy veggie wife an two kids insistin on avin adult portions.

"What's this Vegetable Steak Casserole?" she asks.

"Oh no," I says, "tha's vegetable casserole with steak in it."

"But it does say Vegetable Steak, doesn't it?"

This coulda gone on forever, on'y er ol man tells er t' ave-a veggie lasagne.

Lee's outa is ead as per usual. I reckon ee's on summin, I do.

"One veggie lasagne, but I reckon there's some rat in it somewhere, Martine... Look! There's its brother!" ee yells, pointin is spatula at-a corner of-a kitchens. I twirl round like a ballerina, then give im a shove in is bulbous beer-gut an ee makes out t' swat me like a fly. Mich comes in lookin all excited like she seen some lush pop-star. She catches old o' my arm, while I'm on-a look-out fer ol Thorpey, oo always seems t' rush in when we int workin tidy.

"Martine! There's these really ace boys!... Yew gotta come an give me an and! I'm on pins!"

"Aye, I will, arfta I done this one table. Okay?"

So I takes in the veggie lasagne an the usband's ome-made pie (what comes straight from-a freezer) an ave a gawk. There's a loada tables put together an, jus as Mich said, a pile o' stonkin men and boys in posh suits an flash ties. Then I see Thorpey chattin to an older man oo wuz with em an ee glares over at me, so I make out I'm busy servin the famlee.

As I'm dishin out-a veg, I yer a Merthyr voice an 'n unmistakable one at tha. I practically fling-a veg onto the bloke's lap an spatter im with gravy. The back end o' Dave's ead, I'm shewer.

"Excuse me!" says the bloke.

"Oh, I am sorry!" I grovells, in case ee should call Thorpey. I do a rapid runner back to-a kitchen an grab old o' Mich, oo's gotta andfull o' prawn cocktails.

"Well, Martine, what d'yew think, eh?"

"Mich! Listen! There's this boy I ewsed t' know there... I think theyr Swonzee football team... I gotta do the next servin, right?"

Coz I'm so igh-pitched an wound up, Lee yers me over is sizzlin chip-oil an steak-bashin. Is face is a pumpkin grin.

" Ne' mind the rat, where's the fuckin poison? I could never stick the Jacks!"

"Don' be darft, Lee. Ee's from Merthyr."

"Ey, Mart, I thought yew were a true Bluebird."

"Tha's all in-a past... Right, Mich, give us them prawn cocks!"

Michelle's nearly creamin er knicks on-a spot, she's so worked up.

"Ey, we could be on yer... I fancy the big black one, I do!"

"I gotta black puddin in the fridge, if yew don' get off with im," shouts Lee.

"Shurrup Lee, y' racist dick!" I yells as Mr Thorpe comes bustin through-a door. Ee's tampin an is ard white face its me like a breeze-block.

"Martine," ee whispers snakey, "just get on with the job or you're out! Right?"

I feel like tellin im t' stuff it, but I iss back "Yes Mr Thorpe!" I go calm but quick inta the dinin area an make a point o' servin Dave first. I glance over t' see Mich urryin towards the big black fella, oo looks real chuffed. Dave's busy talkin, so I lean right over im, cranin t' face im like I wuz goin t' give im a peck.

"Yewr prawn cocktail sir!" I says, so deliberate an sarky ee turns straight away, lookin curious till ee recognises me. Is eyes 'n mouth narrow t' three blades. Then ee turns away with a flick o' is ead like ee wuz eadin-a ball or summin.

As I return to-a kitchens I yer im callin me back. I don' wanna respond, but thinkin o' Thorpey's warnin, I decide to.

"Uh... scuse me, waitress, but can I ave my steak well done, please? I carn stand the sight o' blood!"

An all-a players larf, like it woz some private joke.

"Yes, of course, sir!" I feel like spittin out-a words, but I control myself, savin it up. Inside, I'm so angry coz ee treated me like I woz nobody. All is indifference brings it back: ow ee ewsed me against er, er against me. I seen ow ee wanted us t' be total enemies. An I played is game orright... a Stanley knife I on'y brung fer protection... she wuz avin a go at me all-a time... "Martine, yew've lost im, yew bitch! Le's face it, yewr a loser!"... Blood everywhere. Now I gotta remember. Er blood on my clothes an ands: I knew I'd never wash off them stains. An when Dave says bout is steak jus then it seemed aimed, like is sharp eyes shinin.

I decide t' take in these special steak knives we aven ewsed frages an Lee thinks I'm darft.

"Wha yew wanna bother with em for? I need em f' choppin up the rats anyway."

"Lee do me favour an chop yerself up, they'll be one less rat then."

I rub my and cross-a blade o' one. I feel scared an thrilled at-a same time. Mich comes in grinnin all over er body, as if she've orready got tha fella. I old up-a knife towards er.

"Ey, Martine! Go easy! I never spoke to yewrs. Onest!"

"It's okay, Mich. This one's fer im!" I clatter-a knives onto a tray, leavin Michelle stunned.

This time I take it real slow, as if I woz strokin. I know wha I'm doin, so's I asks oo's avin steak an watch is face as I carefully place each knife. I old each one a while before puttin it down an I cun see is panic risin. Ee cun see I'm leavin im till last an ow much I'm relishin it all. Looks as if ee's poopin is pants when I finally come t' im.

"Yew avin steak, sir... Well done, wern it?"

"Er... aye... ta," ee tries t' act so cool, but is ands 're fiddlin with is other cutlery, as if ee's searchin f' weapons!

I take old o' the las steak-knife an prepare t' show im. Now ee'll get the message. I cun take down tha cuttin. I cun wash off tha red. I sweep the knife up to is face an ee jerks back in is chair, nearly fallin. At-a same time, Michelle comes in screamin, "Don' do it, Martine! Don' do it agen!"

An I says t' Dave, real calm... "Is this done enough fer yew sir?"

Ever'thin appens so quick, I think I've sliced im without knowin. Is team-mates 're laughin, Michelle grabs my arm an Thorpey's fussin an pullin me back t' the kitchen. Ee drags me outa the door inta the yard. I still gotta knife, but there's no blood anywhere t' be seen.

"This is no joke, Martine! How dare you treat our customers like this? Who do you think you are? You can't..."

I fling the knife to the ground an-a sound severs is words, leaves em angin.

"Yew cun stick yewr bloody job, Mr Thorpe! An I wozn messin, fer yewr information, it wuz fer real. I owed tha boy one!"

"I should never have taken you on... I knew about your record, you know... They told me you'd changed... Now, get out of my hotel!"

I undo-a apron an scrumple it up as ee shoves past me. I fling it in-a bin an feel a real buzz, though ee never seen me.

As I stride away down-a street, a coach passes an faces stare at me with a "Wow" on theyr lips. All of em cept one, that is. I lost so much to im: my body, my freedom an now my job. I'll go ome an take-a scissors to er photo. Cut it up inta tiny pieces knowin tha won' be the end, but tha problee, this is some kind o' beginnin.